ANDERSEN'S FAIRY TALES

Retold by

ROSE DOBBS

Illustrated by

GUSTAV HJORTLUND

Prepared under the supervision of Josette Frank, Children's Book Adviser
of the Child Study Association of America.

Published in New York by Random House, Inc., and simultaneously
in Toronto, Canada, by Random House of Canada, Limited.

Library of Congress Catalog Card Number: 58-6191

Manufactured in the United States of America

Random House · New York

NOTA

The Emperor's New Clothes

Many years ago there lived an Emperor who was so intensely fond of elegant new clothes that he spent all his money on being well dressed. He paid no attention to his army. He cared nothing about the theater, and if he went for a drive he did so only to show off his fine new clothes. He had a different outfit for each hour of the day, and just as people might say of any king, "He's in conference," so here they always said of the Emperor, "He's dressing."

The Emperor lived in a big city where something exciting was always going on. Strangers came and went all the time, and one day two swindlers appeared. They introduced themselves as weavers and said no one could begin to imagine how exquisite was the material they could weave. And what was more, they declared, not only were their colors and designs uncommonly lovely, but clothes made from the fabrics they wove had a strange power—they became invisible to anyone who was unfit for his office or who was extremely stupid.

"Such clothes might come in handy indeed," thought the Emperor. "If I had some I'd know at once who among my people were not qualified for their jobs. I could also tell immediately which were the clever ones and which the fools. Yes, some of that stuff must be woven for me at once."

And he gave the two swindlers a large advance payment so they could begin to weave without delay.

The rogues put up two looms and made believe they were hard at work, but there was absolutely nothing on the looms. Without batting an eye, they soon demanded the finest silk and the most expensive gold thread, all of which they crammed into their own suitcases. Then they returned to the empty looms and pretended to work until late into the night.

After a while the Emperor wondered how they were getting on. "I'd like to know how much of the material is ready," he thought. But he hesitated to inquire when he remembered that owing to the fabric's strange power one who was either a fool or unfit for his office would not be able to see it. The Emperor was inclined to believe that personally he had nothing to fear; still he thought it might be well to send someone else first to see what progress had been made. The whole city knew about the material's secret power and everyone was eager to find out how stupid or how lacking in ability his neighbor was.

"The very person to send to the weavers," thought the Emperor, "is my honest old minister of state. He'll be best able to judge the material because he has good common sense and no one is better suited to his post than he."

So the honest old minister went off to the workroom where the two swindlers sat at the empty looms.

"Heavens!" he thought, and he opened his eyes wide. "I can't see a thing." But of course he did not say so.

The two rascals begged him to come closer and, pointing to the empty looms, asked what he thought of the colors and the design. The poor old minister opened his eyes wider but he still couldn't see a thing for there was nothing to see.

"Oh merciful Heavens," he said to himself, "is it possible that I'm a fool? Certainly I never thought so and now no one must even suspect it. Or, can it be that I'm unfit for my office? Well . . . obviously I mustn't let any-

one know that I can't see the material."

"Haven't you anything to say? Won't you tell us how you like it?" asked one of the weavers.

"Oh, it's entrancing," answered the old minister, peering harder than ever through his spectacles. "Such an original pattern and such unusual colors! I shall tell the Emperor I am simply enchanted with it."

"We're delighted to hear you say so," said the weavers.

Then they carefully described the intricate design and named all the colors, and the old minister listened attentively so that he could repeat every word to the Emperor. And this he did.

Now the swindlers demanded more cash, more silk, and more gold thread which they said they needed for weaving but which they pocketed themselves. They did not put a single thread on the looms but continued to work at the empty frames as diligently as ever.

Not long after this the Emperor sent another trustworthy official to see how the weavers were coming along and to find out how soon the material would be ready. This one fared no better than the first. Although he gazed and gazed he could see nothing, for there was nothing to see.

"Isn't this the loveliest material imaginable?" asked the swindlers. They pretended to show him the pattern and described the design that wasn't there at all.

"I'm certainly not stupid," thought this official. "Then it must be my wonderful job for which apparently I'm not qualified. This will no doubt amuse a great many people, but I'll make sure they never find out." So he too praised the material he could not see and told the rascals he was more than pleased with the beautiful colors and the splendid design.

"It's absolutely marvelous," he told the Emperor, on his return.

The whole town rang with the news of the gorgeous material and the Emperor decided to see for himself the remarkable fabric while it was still on the looms. So with a large but select company, including the two honest old officials who had already been there, the Emperor sallied forth to visit the weavers. He found the sly imposters working away furiously, although there wasn't a sign of thread on the looms.

"Isn't it magnificent?" asked both the honest old officials. "Will your Majesty deign to note the original design and the glowing colors?" And they pointed to the empty looms, for they thought all the others could see the material.

"What's this?" The Emperor was appalled. "I don't see a thing!" He thought, "How awful! Am I a fool? Am I not fit to be Emperor? Why, that would be the most terrible thing that could happen to me." But aloud he said, "Oh, it is marvelous, simply marvelous. It has my complete royal approval." And he nodded his head to show his satisfaction while he stared and stared at the empty looms, for nothing in the world could make him confess that he didn't see a thing.

The select company stared and stared too but saw no more than he did. However, they all repeated what the Emperor had just said: "Oh, it is marvelous, simply marvelous."

Everyone advised the Emperor to have a new costume made from this wonderful cloth and to wear it in the State Procession that was soon to take place. "Magnificent!" "Sumptuous!" "Grand!" were some of the words the enthusiastic company used to describe the material. The Emperor knighted the swindlers, gave each the title of Sir Knight of the Loom, and presented both with little emblems of their new order to wear in their buttonholes.

The night before the procession, the swindlers worked from dusk to dawn, burning sixteen candles. All could see how eager they were to finish the Emperor's new clothes. They pretended to take the cloth off the looms and with big scissors they slashed away at the air as if they were cutting out a pattern. Then they sewed for hours and hours, without a bit of thread in their needles. At last they proclaimed the clothes ready.

Accompanied by the most illustrious members of the Court, the Emperor himself then arrived and the swindlers met him, each with outstretched arms as if he were holding something.

"Here," they said, "are your Imperial Majesty's royal breeches, and this is the coat, and this the cloak. These garments are light as air. Indeed, their wearer might almost think he had nothing on, but that's just why they're so remarkable."

"Yes," agreed all the most illustrious members of the Court, but they saw nothing, for there was nothing to see.

"Will your Imperial Majesty be pleased to take off your clothes so that we may help you put on the new clothes, here in front of this full-length mirror?" asked the swindlers.

So the Emperor took off his clothes and the imposters pretended to hand him, one by one, the various pieces of his new outfit. They made believe they pinned something here and adjusted something there and finally pretended to tie on the train. And the Emperor preened, turning this way and that before the mirror.

"What an exquisite costume! How well it fits! Such a perfect cut and *such* colors!" said all the courtiers. "It's positively and unquestionably fit only for royalty."

"Your Majesty's procession canopy is waiting outside," said the master of ceremonies.

"Very well," said the Emperor. "I take it I'm ready. Yes, don't the new clothes fit me well?" And once more he turned this way and that before the mirror, for he wanted all the court to see how carefully he inspected his new clothes.

The two attendants who were to carry the train stooped down and pretended to lift it off the floor. Then they held their hands out high as if they were really carrying a train, for they didn't dare let anyone think that they knew there was no train to carry.

And so the procession started out with the Emperor under the resplendent canopy, and along the way all the people lining the streets or watching from their windows said, "What elegant new clothes!" And, "How beautifully they fit!" No one would admit he could see nothing, for that would be admitting he was a fool or that he was unfit for his job. Never before had the Emperor worn clothes that met with such wholehearted approval.

"But he's got nothing on," marvelled a little child.

"Ah, just listen to this innocent one," said its father.

And one person began to whisper to another, "He's got nothing on. A little child says he's got nothing on."

"But he *has* nothing on," cried everyone at last.

A chill went down the Emperor's spine. It seemed to him the people were right. "But the show must go on," he told himself. So he drew himself up as tall as he could and walked proudly on, his head high; and the attendants held on for dear life to the train that didn't even exist.

The Nightingale

Of course you know that the Emperor of China is a Chinese, and everyone around him is Chinese too. This story happened many years ago but that is just why it should be written down before it's forgotten.

The Emperor's palace was the most exquisite thing in the world. It was made entirely of porcelain, expensive and fine. The most unusual flowers bloomed in the garden and to the rarest and prettiest were tied little silver bells which tinkled constantly. The garden itself was so vast that even the gardener had no idea where it ended. If you kept on walking you would come to a lovely woods. The woods went down to the deep blue sea where big ships could sail in right under the overhanging branches of the trees. And among these trees lived a nightingale.

This nightingale sang so gloriously that the poor fisherman, a busy man, would pause in his labors to listen. He would sigh and say, "How lovely that is!"

From near and far, from every country in the world, came travelers to wonder at the Emperor's city and his palace and his garden; but when they heard the nightingale they all agreed this was the most marvelous of all the Emperor's marvels. When they returned to their homes the travelers couldn't stop talking about the wonders they had seen, and in all the countries learned men wrote many books about the Emperor's city, his porcelain palace, his endless garden, and the nightingale. Oh, they did not forget the nightingale; in fact, they all said—right in print—"And the nightingale is the best of all."

Now these books went all over the world and in the course of time a few reached the Emperor. He sat in his golden chair and read for hours, now and then nodding approvingly, for the glowing accounts pleased him very much. "And the nightingale is the best of all," said every book.

The Emperor read it himself—right there in print. "What's this?" he cried. "What's all this about a nightingale, here in my own garden? I know nothing of such a bird. Why hasn't anyone told me about it? Imagine my having to learn a thing like this from a book!"

With that he at once called his First Lord-in-Waiting, an individual so exalted that if any person of lower rank so much as dared to address him or presumed to ask him a question, he would only answer, "P!" And that meant exactly nothing.

"All the books say there's a wonderful bird here called a nightingale," the Emperor said. "They say this nightingale is the best thing in my whole kingdom. Why haven't I been told about the nightingale?"

"I've never heard its name mentioned before," said the First Lord-in-Waiting. "No doubt the bird has not been presented at Court."

"I command the bird to appear before me this very

evening and to sing for me," said the Emperor. "A fine how-do-you-do! The whole world knows everything about this fabulous possession of mine and I know nothing."

"I've never heard its name mentioned before," said the First Lord-in-Waiting again, "but I'll go look for the nightingale directly. I'll find it."

Yes, that was easier said than done. Where was the nightingale to be found? The First Lord-in-Waiting turned the palace inside out. Upstairs and downstairs he ran, into every room and through each hall and corridor. But he didn't find the nightingale. He didn't even find anyone who had so much as heard of the nightingale. So he hurried back to the Emperor and told him the books must be lying. "Your Majesty shouldn't believe everything you see written in books," he said. "You know how writers are—they all like to make up fantastic stories."

"But I read about the nightingale in a book sent me by the high and mighty Emperor of Japan," said the Emperor, "so it can't be a lie. I *will* hear the nightingale sing. It *must* be brought here this very evening. I have bestowed my gracious Imperial favor upon it, but if it doesn't show up, then I'll make it my business to see that every member of the Court gets a good swift kick right after supper."

"Tsing-pe!" exclaimed the First Lord-in-Waiting. And once more he began to search every nook and cranny. He ran upstairs and down; he investigated each passageway and hall. With him went half the Court, for no one relished the idea of getting a good swift kick right after supper.

At last, in the kitchen, they found a poor little scullery maid who said, "The nightingale? Why yes, I know the nightingale. It does sing beautifully. Every evening I am allowed to take a few scraps from the table to my sick mother who lives near the shore. On my way back I sometimes stop to

rest in the woods and then I hear the nightingale. Its singing brings tears to my eyes—it's as if my mother's kissing me."

"Little scullery maid," said the First Lord-in-Waiting, "I will see that you get a steady job in the kitchen and will even arrange to have permission granted you to watch the Emperor dine if you'll take us to the nightingale. We must find it, for the Emperor has commanded it to appear this very evening and sing before him."

So the little scullery maid led him, with half the Court, to the woods where the nightingale lived. As they went along a cow began to moo.

"Oh," cried all the courtiers, "there's the nightingale singing. What a powerful voice for so small a creature! Yes, we've certainly heard this song before."

"No, no," said the little scullery maid. "That's a cow, mooing. We still have a long way to go."

They walked on and soon they heard frogs croaking in a marsh.

"Enchanting," said the Court chaplain. "I can hear the nightingale now. Its singing is just like the tinkling of church bells."

"No, no," said the little scullery maid. "That's frogs, croaking. But we're close now and I think we'll hear the nightingale any minute."

Just then the nightingale started to sing. "That's it!" exclaimed the little scullery maid. "Listen; oh listen! And there—there it is!" And she pointed to a little gray bird 'way up in one of the high branches of a tree.

"Is it possible?" said the First Lord-in-Waiting. "Who would have thought it would look like this? What an ordinary creature! And so colorless, though I dare say it's probably turned pale at seeing so many distinguished people here."

"Little nightingale," the scullery maid called up loudly to the bird, "our gracious Emperor wants to hear you sing."

"With pleasure," said the nightingale, and it began to trill away in the most delightful manner.

"It's exactly like glass bells," said the First Lord-in-Waiting. "And see how its tiny throat is throbbing. I wonder why we've never heard of this bird before. What a hit it will make at Court!"

"Shall I sing to the Emperor again?" asked the nightingale, for it thought the Emperor was there among all the company.

"My excellent little nightingale," said the First Lord-in-Waiting, "I have the honor to command you to appear at a Court recital this evening where you shall enchant his Imperial Majesty with your remarkable singing."

"My singing sounds best in the woods," said the nightingale. However, it went willingly with them when it understood that was the Emperor's wish.

A golden perch had been placed for the nightingale in the middle of the grand hall where the whole Court had assembled and where the Emperor sat on his throne. The little scullery maid, who had been promoted to the position of Regular-Worker-in-the-Palace-Kitchen, was allowed to watch from behind the kitchen door. Everyone was magnificently dressed and all stared at the modest little bird in simple gray. The Emperor nodded graciously to it and the nightingale began to sing, so gloriously that tears welled up in the Emperor's eyes and ran down his cheeks. The nightingale sang again, even more beautifully, and the song went straight to the Emperor's heart. He was so delighted with the performance that he wanted to reward the nightingale, so he offered it his golden slipper to wear around its neck. But the nightingale declined the honor and told the Emperor it had already received its reward.

"I have seen tears in the Emperor's eyes," it said. "That is reward enough for me."

There was no question about it—the nightingale was a huge success. It had a cage all to itself and was allowed to go out twice during the day and once during the night. Whenever it went out, though, twelve servants went with it, each of them holding on tightly to a silken ribbon tied to the bird's leg. You can see that there wasn't much fun to such outings.

One day a large box arrived for the Emperor. The label on the box said: THE NIGHTINGALE. "Ah," remarked the Emperor, "no doubt this is another learned book about our famous bird." There wasn't a book at all, but a pretty toy in the box, an artificial nightingale skillfully copied after the real one but studded all over with diamonds and rubies and sapphires. When the bird was wound up it sang one of the real nightingale's songs, and as it warbled its little tail waggled up and down shimmering with gold and silver. Around its neck it wore a ribbon on which was written: *The Emperor of Japan's nightingale is a poor thing beside the Emperor of China's nightingale.*

"It's simply wonderful," said all the people of the Court, and the man who had brought it was immediately given the title of Imperial-Nightingale-Bringer-in-Chief.

"Let's have them sing together," said someone. "That will be a duet worth hearing."

But the duet didn't sound well because the real nightingale sang in its own free way while the artificial one could sing only the one mechanical tune.

"It's really no fault of our bird," said the music master. "It can keep perfect time and it sings just as it's been constructed to sing."

So the mechanical bird now sang alone and made as great a hit as the real one had. Besides, it was so much more glamorous because it glittered like so many bracelets and brooches.

The bird sang its one tune over and over again—thirty-three times in all—and never tired. The whole Court would have liked to hear it still again but the Emperor thought the real nightingale should now have a chance to sing again. But where was it? Without anyone's noticing, it had flown out of the window back to its own green woods.

"Why should it want to do that?" asked the Emperor, puzzled.

All the Court declared the nightingale was an ungrateful wretch. "However, it's no great loss," said everyone. "After all, we do have the best bird."

The real nightingale was banished from the kingdom—exiled—and the artificial one was given a place of

honor in the Emperor's bedroom. It sat on a silken cushion on the left side of his bed. For the Emperor considered the side on which the heart is located to be the more important one and even an Emperor's heart is on the left side. All the beautiful presents that the bird had received, all the gold and jewels, lay around it. It now bore the title of Chief-Imperial-Singer-to-Sleep-of-the-Emperor. The music master wrote a whole series of books about the bird—twenty-five volumes, in fact.

Well, things went on like this for a whole year. The Emperor, the Court, and every other person in the land now knew by heart every trill, every twitter of the bird's one song. The little street urchins sang it and even the Emperor himself often joined in.

One evening when the Emperor was lying in bed listening to the bird who was singing its very best, something suddenly went *whirr* and *whizz* inside the bird. A spring snapped, the wheels spun round and round, and the music stopped. The Emperor leaped out of bed and called for his own personal physician, but what could *he* do? So a watchmaker was summoned and after a good deal of hemming and hawing and poking about, the bird was more or less put together again. The watchmaker said the bearings were badly worn out and that from now on the bird would have to be handled with care and not played too often for then it would break down altogether. He said it would be impossible to replace the worn-out parts without damaging the music. What a disappointment this was! The nightingale now sang only once a year on special occasions.

Five years went by and a great sorrow filled the land. The people were really fond of their Emperor who now lay very ill. It was said he had not long to live and a new emperor had already been chosen. People gathered in little groups in the palace courtyard and asked the First Lord-in-Waiting how the Emperor was feeling. "P," was all *he* would say and shook his head.

The Emperor lay wan and cold in his splendid bed and the whole Court thought he was dead. So they hurried away to greet the new emperor. But the Emperor was not dead. It was very quiet in the room. One of the

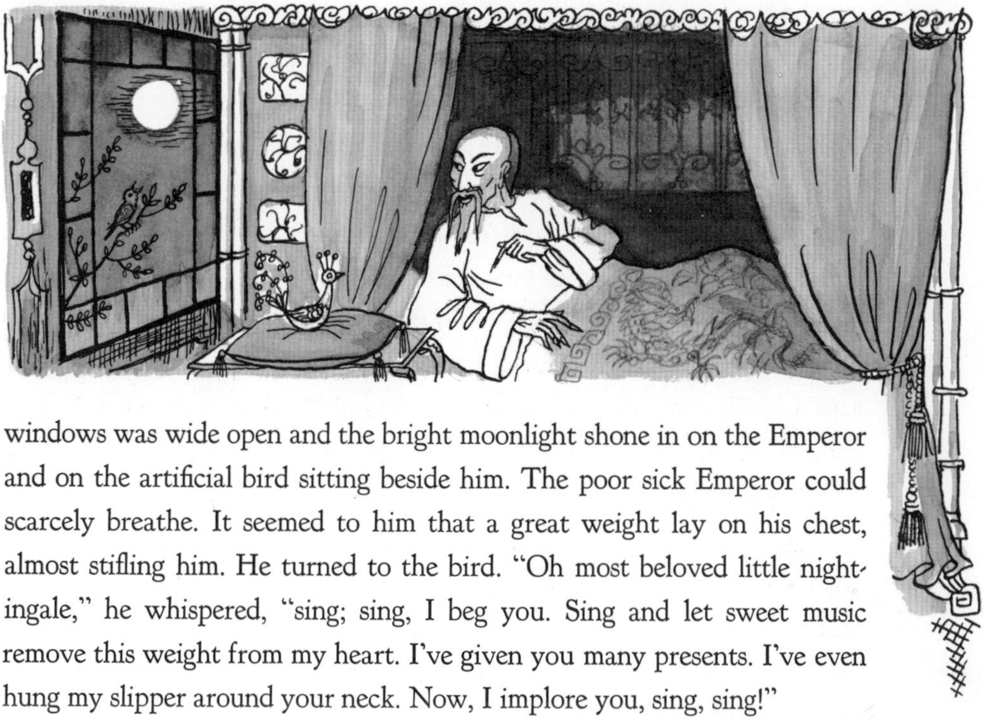

windows was wide open and the bright moonlight shone in on the Emperor and on the artificial bird sitting beside him. The poor sick Emperor could scarcely breathe. It seemed to him that a great weight lay on his chest, almost stifling him. He turned to the bird. "Oh most beloved little nightingale," he whispered, "sing; sing, I beg you. Sing and let sweet music remove this weight from my heart. I've given you many presents. I've even hung my slipper around your neck. Now, I implore you, sing, sing!"

The bird never moved. There was no one to wind it up so it couldn't sing a note. The weight on the Emperor's chest grew heavier and heavier; the room became quieter and quieter. Suddenly from the open window came the most enchanting music. The real nightingale sat outside on a branch of a tree. It had heard of the Emperor's need and had come to sing to him of hope and to comfort him with lovely music. And as it sang the weight on the Emperor's chest began to rise. The bird sang of peace and quiet rest and the healing fragrance of roses and lilacs.

"Thank you, thank you," cried the Emperor. "I know you now, you heavenly little bird. I banished you from my kingdom, yet you have come to help me. Your beautiful singing has lifted the dreadful weight from my heart. How can I ever repay you?"

"You have already paid me well," said the nightingale. "The first time I sang to you your eyes filled with tears. I can never forget that. But now, go to sleep while I sing to you, and awake refreshed and strong."

So the bird sang while the Emperor drifted off into a deep, refreshing sleep. When he awoke he felt well and strong. The sun shone in on him and the nightingale still sat there outside his window, singing. None of his attendants was there, for they all believed him dead.

"Please don't ever leave me," the Emperor said to the nightingale. "You must stay here with me always. You shall sing whenever and whatever you please, and as for this other bird, I'll smash it to bits!"

"No, you mustn't do that," said the nightingale. "The poor thing did the best it could. Keep it. But as for me, I cannot build my nest and live in a palace. I'll come to you often, though, and I'll perch here outside your window and sing to you. But you must promise me one thing."

"Gladly," said the Emperor, "anything you wish."

"Only one thing I would ask," said the nightingale. "Don't ever let anyone know that you have a little bird to tell you things. It will be better that way." And the nightingale flew away.

The servants came in to attend to their dead Emperor—and stood stock-still! The Emperor looked at them and said, "Good morning!"

Five in One Pod

Five peas lived in one pod. The peas were green and the pod was green, so naturally they thought the whole world was green. The pod grew and the peas grew; they made themselves as comfortable as they could and sat close together in a row. The bright sun warmed the shell and the gentle rain turned it smooth and clear. It was quite cosy, there in the pod, and the peas sat on, growing bigger and bigger and thinking harder and harder as they grew, for of course they had to have something to do.

At last one spoke up: "Are we to sit here forever? I'm afraid we'll all grow calloused from too much sitting still in one place. It seems to me something is going on outside—I can smell it."

Weeks went by. The pod grew yellow and the peas grew yellow. "The whole world's turning yellow," they said, and they had a perfect right to say so.

All of a sudden they felt a tug. The pod was pulled apart, the shell torn off. It was held a moment in a human hand; then it was pushed into a jacket pocket already crammed with bulging pods.

"It won't be long now before we're opened," said the peas, and they could hardly contain themselves until the time came.

"I wonder which of us will become the most remarkable," said the smallest of the five. "But we'll soon find out."

"What will be, will be," said the largest pea.

Pop! The pod burst open and all five peas rolled out into the bright sunshine. A little boy clutched them; he said they were just what he needed for his peashooter, and immediately he put one of the peas into the peashooter and let fly.

"Here I go," cried the pea, "flying out into the wide world! Catch me if you can." And he was gone.

"I," said the second, "shall aim straight for the sun. *There's* a pod for you—and it'll suit me fine!" And *he* was gone.

"We needn't exert ourselves," said the next two, "because we'll get wherever we're going anyway and no doubt we'll keep rolling along." Indeed, they tumbled down and rolled on the ground but it did them no good for they got into the peashooter just the same. "*We'll* make the biggest splash," they said.

"What will be, will be," said the last as he went flying out of the peashooter. He shot up to an old board under a garret window and landed in a crack filled with moss and soft mold. There he lay, alone, and hidden by the moss—forgotten by all except kind old frugal Mother Nature.

"What will be, will be," he said.

In the garret lived a poor woman and her little daughter. The mother went out to work every day. She cleaned stoves, chopped wood, and did not hesitate to do even more strenuous work for she was strong and tireless. But although she worked very hard, she remained poor.

At home in the garret lay her only child, the little daughter who had been ill for a whole year and who showed no signs of improving. Sadly the mother thought she would never get well. All day long the little sick girl lay in her bed, without complaining, while her mother was at work.

Early one spring morning, just as the mother was about to leave, the sun came through the window and threw bright rays across the floor. The sick child turned her eyes on the lowest pane of glass.

"There's a little green thing looking in at the window," she said. "See, it's swaying in the wind. What can it be?"

The mother went to the window and raised it a bit. "Why, it's a tiny plant," she said. "A pea plant. It's taken root and has already put out green leaves. I wonder how it got here. But never mind—it makes a nice little garden to keep you company."

She moved the child's bed closer to the window so that she could watch the gallant little plant and went off to work.

That evening the invalid was all excited. "Mother, I believe I'm going to get well," she said. "All day long the sun has been warming both me and the little plant. It's coming along fine and so am I. I know I'll be able to get up soon and perhaps even go out into the sunshine."

"Oh, if only God would grant it," sighed the mother. But she really did not believe such a miracle could happen. However, so that it might stand up against the wind, she took a little stick and carefully propped up the plant that had so cheered her child and had given her a desire to live. She tied a piece of string from the window sill to the upper part of the window frame. Now the little pea had somewhere to climb.

"Oh, look," cried the mother one morning, "our little plant has a flower!" And now she dared hope that her sick child would get well at last.

About a week later, the child was able to get up for the first time and to sit for a whole hour in the warm sunshine. The window was wide open, and there outside, as if welcoming her, was a fully blown pink pea blossom. The little girl leaned over and gently kissed the fragrant petals. It was a day for celebrating.

"God himself planted the pea, my darling," said the happy mother. "He made it flourish and grow so that it would bring joy and courage to you—and to me, too." And she smiled at the pea as if it were a messenger from Heaven.

And now—what about the other peas? Well, the first one, he who went flying out into the wide world crying, "Catch me if you can," landed on a rooftop where a pigeon made short work of him. The next two, the lazy ones, met with a similar fate and were also gobbled up by pigeons. At least, they served *some* purpose. But the fourth, the ambitious one who was going to fly to the sun, that one landed in the gutter. He lay there in the dirty water for days on end, swelling up more and more.

"How stylishly stout I'm becoming," he said. "In the end I must burst and more than this no pea can hope to accomplish. There's no doubt about it—I'm the most remarkable of the five of us who lived in the one pod." The gutter thought he was absolutely right.

But at the garret window stood the little girl, her eyes shining, her cheeks glowing with health. She folded her slim hands over the pretty pea flower and thanked God for it.

Whatever the Old Man Does Is Right

This story is very old. I first heard it when I was a child and the more I think of it the better I like it. For some stories are like some people—the older they get, the nicer they become, and this is a pleasant thought indeed.

Well, then, it seems that once upon a time there lived in a modest little cottage out in the country an old peasant and his wife. They were rich only in their love for each other. Of things they had little; still they decided they could do with one thing less—their horse. He was all right as horses go, managing as best he could by nibbling the grass that grew beside the road. Sometimes the peasant rode him into town, and now and then his neighbors would borrow the horse and in return would do the peasant a small favor or two.

Nevertheless, the old couple felt they could sell the horse for a good price; if not, they could surely exchange him for something better. What should it be? Sell? Exchange?

"You'll know what to do, my good man," said the wife. "This is market day, isn't it? Why not ride the horse into town and either sell him or make a good trade? Whatever you decide will be right."

And she tied his neckerchief for him—she was handier than he at this—and made it fast with a double knot. Carefully she dusted off his hat, set it on his head, gave him a kiss and a pat and sent him off on his way, riding the horse he was either to sell or trade in. Of course, whatever he decided to do was sure to be right.

The sun beat fiercely down; there wasn't a cloud in the sky. The road was jammed with people going to market, some in wagons, some on horseback, some on foot, all raising up a thick veil of dust. And not a speck of shade anywhere.

Presently the peasant spied a man driving a cow, as nice a cow as anyone could wish.

"I'll wager she gives good milk," he thought. "If I could trade my horse for that cow, I'd be making a fine exchange." And he called out to the man: "You there—you with the cow. I'd like a word with you." The man stopped, and the peasant said, "No doubt a horse is worth more than a cow. Yet it happens that I have need of a cow. Would you care to exchange?"

"Suits me," said the man. So they traded animals and each felt he had made a good bargain.

Having accomplished what he had set out to do, the peasant could have turned around and started off for home, but he had made up his mind to go to market, and go to market he would, just to look around.

So he continued on his way, with the cow, stepping along at a brisk pace. Soon he overtook a man leading a sheep—a very fine sheep with a good healthy thick coat of wool.

"My, I'd like to have that sheep," the peasant thought. "There's plenty of grass along our road for her to eat and in the winter she could stay in our room. Yes, it would be much better for us to have a sheep than a cow."

So he said to the fellow with the sheep:

"How about making a trade? My cow for your sheep."

"Done," said the other, and the exchange was made.

The peasant trudged on, with the sheep, and presently he came alongside a man carrying a big fat goose under his arm.

"Quite a bundle you've got there," he said, "full of feathers and fat. That goose would look fine, tied up near our little pond. Besides, it would give my old wife a good reason to save scraps. She has often wished for a goose. Perhaps now she can have her wish. What do you say? How about trading your goose for my sheep, and my thanks thrown in."

The other was willing, so the exchange was made.

By this time the peasant was close to the town and growing a little weary. The sun got hotter every minute; the crowd larger. People and cattle pushed and shoved this way and that, filling the high road and spilling out and across the ditch right into the toll-keeper's vegetable garden where his only hen was tied up. It was rather a pretty little hen, with short tail feathers, and it winked one eye and said, "Cluck, cluck." What was in the hen's mind when she did this I cannot say, but I can say what was in the peasant's mind when he saw her.

"That's the prettiest hen ever," he thought. "Much prettier even than our parson's brood hen. My, I'd like to have her. A hen is no trouble at all to keep. She can practically take care of herself and can always find something to eat. I wonder if I wouldn't do well to exchange this goose for the hen." And to the toll-keeper he said:

"How about it? Would you exchange your hen for my goose here?"

"Why not?" said the toll-keeper. "It looks like a fair exchange to me."

So he took the goose and the peasant got the hen.

It had been quite a day. What with the heat, and the crowds, and the walking, and all the bargaining he had done, the peasant was now really very tired. He longed for a bite to eat and a cool drink, and he turned his steps toward an inn. He was just about to enter it when the innkeeper appeared in the doorway, carrying a huge sack chock-full of something.

"What's in that sack?" inquired the peasant.

"Rotten apples," said the innkeeper. "Gobs of rotten apples. Enough to feed all the pigs."

"What a tremendous lot of apples it is!" said the peasant. "I'll bet my wife would like to see so many. Last year our old tree at home gave us but one single solitary apple. How my wife treasured it! She said owning the apple made us rich, but here are riches indeed. Ah, how I wish she could see these."

"Well," said the innkeeper, "if you want them so much, what will you give me in return?"

"Why, I'll give you my hen," cried the peasant.

The innkeeper knew a bargain when he saw one, so the exchange was quickly made. He took the hen and the peasant picked up the sack of rotten apples, entered the inn, and went straight up to the bar. Here he set the sack down on the floor, propping it up against the stove, not realizing that the stove was piping hot.

Among the people in the room were many strangers, including two Englishmen. They were so rich that their pockets were bulging with money. Like most Englishmen you read about they loved to make wagers and presently they made a very fancy one—as you shall hear.

Above all the noise and talk in the room there soon rose another sound. It came from the stove and it said, "Sss. Sss."

"What can that be?" asked everyone.

One question led to another and before long the whole story of the day's bargaining came out: how the horse had been exchanged for the cow and the cow for the goose and the goose for the hen and the hen for a sack full of rotten apples that were even now roasting there by the stove and saying, "Sss. Sss."

"Oh boy," said one of the Englishmen. "Won't you catch it when you get home! Your wife will beat you black and blue."

"On the contrary," said the peasant. "I'll get kisses, not blows. My wife always says, 'Whatever the old man does is right,' and I'll wager she'll say it now too."

"You'll wager?" cried the Englishman. "That's fine. I'll take up your wager, and let it be in gold coin by the barrel—a hundred pounds to the hundredweight."

"By the bushel will be enough," said the peasant. "Besides, I can wager only this sack of rotten apples, though I dare say if I throw in myself and my old woman it will make a fair full measure. Shall we say good enough and done?"

"Good enough and done," said the Englishman, and the bet was on.

The innkeeper ordered his cart brought out and all piled into it—the two Englishmen, the peasant, the sack full of rotten apples—and before long they were at the peasant's door.

"Good evening, dear wife," said the peasant.

"A good evening to you, my old man," said the wife.

"I've made the exchange," he told her.

"I'm sure it was a good one," said she. She gave him a hug and never noticed the Englishmen and the sack of apples in the cart.

"I exchanged the horse for a cow," the peasant went on.

"A cow!" exclaimed the wife. "How wonderful! Now we shall have fresh milk every day. That was a very smart deal."

"Yes—well—but I exchanged the cow for a sheep," said he.

"What could be better?" asked the wife. "Trust you to think of everything. We can have sheep's milk and cheese and warm woolen stockings. A cow couldn't give us those. How clever of you."

"Ah yes, well—but—I exchanged the sheep for a goose!"

"Oh, better and better," said the wife. "How thoughtful you are—always planning a nice surprise for me. Won't it be delightful to look for-

ward to a delicious meal of roast goose? We'll fatten the goose up a bit first, and—"

"But I exchanged the goose for a hen," the peasant said.

"A hen! Well. Well. That's the best of all," the wife said. "The hen will lay eggs, hatch them, and before we know it we'll have a little chicken farm. That's what I really want most of all."

"But I gave the hen away for a sack of rotten apples," said the peasant.

"Did you really?" cried the wife. "Then I must give you a kiss. And now I'll tell you something. After you left this morning, I thought I'd have a real good supper for you when you got back. I wanted to make you an omelet with herbs. I had the eggs, but no herbs—not even a smidgeon of chives or a stalk of parsley. So I went over to the schoolmaster's house—they have a nice little herb garden there—and although I know the schoolmistress is stingy, I asked her to lend me a few stalks of this and that.

" 'Lend you,' she cried. 'I haven't anything to lend you. Nothing grows here, not even a rotten apple. I couldn't even lend you that.' So just think of it, husband, *now* I can lend her, not one but at least ten rotten apples. Oh, what a dear, good, thoughtful man you are. Yes, as I've always said, whatever you do is right!"

And she gave him a big hearty kiss.

At this the Englishmen jumped down from the cart.

"Always rolling down hill," they said, "but keeping merry and gay.

It's worth something to see a sight like this."

So they paid the bet cheerfully and the peasant got a whole bushel of gold coins because his wife did not scold him, but kissed and praised him instead.

There, that's the story, and you can see what a good point it makes. It always pays for a wife to let the whole world think the old man is the wiser of the two and that whatever he does is right.

The Flying Trunk

Once upon a time there was a merchant who had so much money that he could have paved a whole street and had enough left over for a little alley. But he didn't do that; he had better use for his gold. When he spent a quarter, he got back a dollar—that's the kind of businessman he was. And he continued to build his fortune until he died.

Now his son got all the money, and a gay, merry life he led. He went to the theater every evening, made kites out of dollar bills, and played ducks and drakes on the lake with gold pieces instead of pebbles. Well, money used like this soon goes, and his went. At last he had nothing left but a few pennies, an old dressing gown, and a pair of worn-out slippers. Naturally, his friends now couldn't be bothered with him; they didn't even want to be seen on the street with him. But one of them, a rather good-natured fellow, sent him a trunk with a note that said, "Take a hint; pack up and leave." This was all very well, but he didn't have a thing to pack, so he got into the trunk himself.

Listen, that was no ordinary trunk. Oh no. When you pressed the lock, the trunk took off. The young man did so and *wheee!* there he was, flying over chimneys and through clouds, farther and farther away. Now and then the trunk creaked a little and he knew a moment of fear. What if it should fall apart! Wouldn't he find himself turning a fine somersault! However, the trunk stayed in one piece until it came down in the land of the Turks. The young man hid the trunk in a woods and then made off for the town. Nobody remarked about his costume for here everyone wore the same thing he did—a dressing gown and slippers. Arrived at the town, he met a nurse with a little child.

"Hi there, Turkish nanny," he said, "can you tell me what that castle is—the one right there with all those high windows?"

"Oh, that's the home of the Sultan's daughter," said the nurse. "It's been foretold that she will have an unhappy love affair so no one is allowed to visit her unless her mother and father are with her."

"Thank you," said the merchant's son. He went back to the woods, got into his trunk, and flew straight to the roof of the Princess's tower. He crept through a window into the room and saw her, asleep on a sofa. She looked so pretty that he couldn't help giving her a kiss. At this she awoke and regarded him in alarm. But he told her that he was the chief magician of the Turks and that he had flown through the air to get to her. This pleased her and they sat down together. Then he told her the most wonderful stories, about her eyes and her forehead and about the storks who

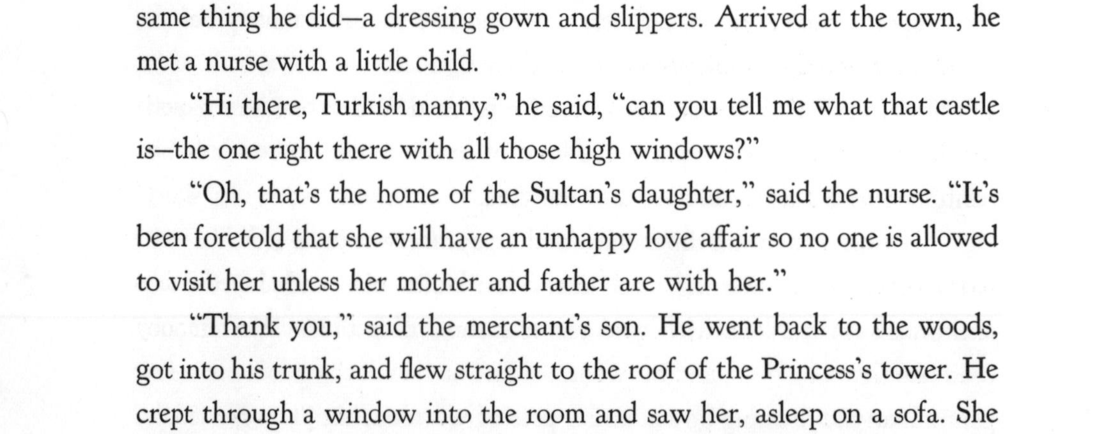

bring the dear little children. Oh, he was quite a storyteller, so that when he finally finished and asked her to marry him, she promptly said Yes. "Come back on Saturday," she said, "when my parents will be here for tea. They'll be so proud to know that I'm to marry the chief magician of the Turks. But you must be sure to have a story for them because they both love stories. My mother prefers one that's serious and points a moral but my father likes a merry tale, one that can make him laugh."

"Fine," said he, "I'll be here on Saturday and I'll bring no other wedding present but a good story." And he bade the Princess good-by. Before he left she gave him a jeweled sword.

He flew off and bought himself an elegant new dressing gown and returned to the woods to compose a story. After all, it had to be ready by Saturday and it's no easy matter to come up with a good story on short notice. However, when Saturday arrived, the story was ready.

The Sultan and his wife and all the fine ladies and gentlemen of the Court were at the Princess's for tea and everyone made the merchant's son welcome.

"Have you a story for us?" asked the Sultan's wife. "One that has something worth-while to say and that can teach us a lesson?"

"Yes," said the Sultan, "but also one that is entertaining and that can make us laugh."

"I have indeed," said the young man, and he began the story directly. Let's draw close and listen too:

Once there was a bundle of Matches and these Matches were very proud because they were of noble birth. The Matches lived now on a kitchen shelf between a Tinder Box and an old iron cooking Pot and they loved to talk to these two about their splendid past when they were young.

"Ah," they sighed, "in those days when we were a branch of the living tree, we truly lived right. Nothing less than diamond tea—you call it dewdrops—twice a day, morning and evening, for us; sunshine all day long; and the little birds to bring us all the latest news. Anyone could see how wealthy we were, for the other trees could afford to dress in green only in the summertime, but the least member of our family wore green all year round. Well, then came the bad times. Woodcutters arrived and there was a great revolution and our family was cut up. Our leader was given a position as mainmast on a fine ship that could go around the whole world if she so wished; the others were sent here and there; and as for us, it became our duty to provide light to the common herd. That is how people of quality come down in the world, and that is why we now find ourselves here in this kitchen."

"Fate has dealt differently with me," said the Pot. "Ever since I first saw the light of day, it's been nothing but cooking and scrubbing and scouring for me. But I take a practical view of things and I know how important I am in this house. My greatest pleasure is to take it easy after dinner when, sitting in my place, scoured and gleaming, I can hold an intelligent conversation with my neighbors. But except for the Water Bucket who sometimes

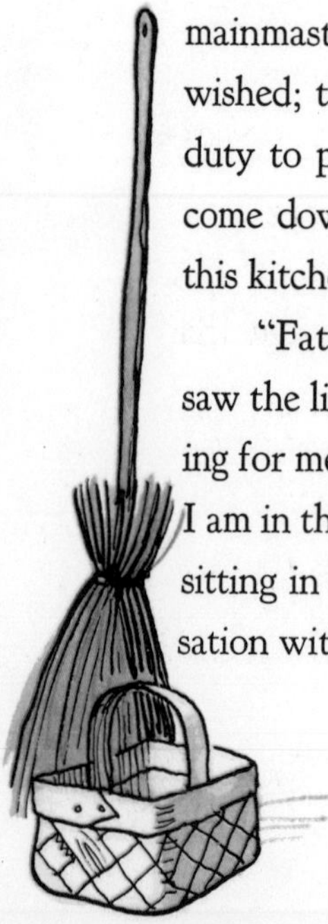

goes out to the yard, all the rest spend most of the time indoors. The only one who ever brings us any news is the Market Basket. But he's always ranting about the Government and the People. Why, the other day he spoke so wildly that an old conservative—that pot over there—alarmed by what he was saying, fell down and smashed to bits. He's a radical, all right, that Market Basket."

"Golly, how you rattle on," said the Tinder Box, and the steel struck against the flint, making the sparks fly. "Come on, let's cheer up."

"Yes. Let's talk about which of us comes from the most aristocratic family," said the Matches.

"No, I don't like to talk about myself," said a little earthenware Jar. "Let's arrange a program for the evening's entertainment and let each of us contribute something to it. . . . Along the shores of the Baltic, where the beech trees of Denmark . . ."

"That's a fine beginning," cried all the Plates. "Just the way we like it."

"Well, that's where I spent my youth, with a respectable family. The furniture was always highly polished, the floors scrubbed, and the curtains were changed every other week."

"How well you tell a story," said the Broom. "One can always tell when a story is related by a lady—there's such an air of refinement about it."

"Yes, we can see that at once," said the Pail, and it gave a little hop-skip of pleasure which sent the water in it splashing all over the floor.

The Jar went on with her story and the end was every bit as good as the beginning.

All the Plates clattered with delight and the Broom crowned the Jar with a parsley wreath. He knew this would annoy the others but he thought, "If I crown her tonight, she'll crown me tomorrow."

"I'm next," said the Fire Tongs, "and I shall do my dance." And so she did. How she danced! She kicked one leg up so high in the air that the Slip Cover on the old chair in the corner almost split to see it. "How about a wreath for me?" the Fire Tongs cried, and so she too was crowned.

"They're nothing but common trash," thought the Matches.

The Teapot was then supposed to give them a song but she refused, saying she had the sniffles. Besides, she pointed out, she couldn't possibly sing unless Boiling Water was there. She was putting on airs because she thought it beneath her to sing anywhere except in the parlor before the master and the mistress.

In the window-seat lay an old quill Pen that the servant girl sometimes used. There was nothing outstanding about this Pen but he had been dipped in the ink too far and this made him very proud. "Let the Teapot alone," he said. "Who cares if she sings or doesn't sing? Outside this window hangs a cage with a nightingale in it. I'm sure he'll be glad to sing for us. You must remember, though, that he hasn't had a chance to prepare anything special, so tonight we'll have to overlook any flaws in his performance."

"I don't approve of this at all," cried the Tea Kettle who was the kitchen's regular singer and a half-sister of the Teapot. "Why should we listen to a foreign singer? Is that being patriotic? Let the Market Basket decide."

"I'm disgusted," said the Market Basket. "I'm disgusted with all of you. Is this your idea of spending a profitable evening? Wouldn't it be better if we cleaned up this mess? Come on, everyone pitch in and I'll supervise you all. Then we'll see some real action!"

"Yes," they all cried, "let's go to town."

Just then the door opened and the servant girl came in. No one moved but there wasn't a pot there who didn't have a high opinion of himself and his abilities. "Yes," each thought, "if I had really wanted to, I could have turned this into quite a jolly night!"

The servant girl took the Matches and put them to the fire. My word, how they flared up and blazed away! "Now," they thought, "this common riffraff can see that we're really the distinguished ones here. How we sparkle! What a brilliant light we shed!" And then they burned out.

"That was a capital story," said the Sultan's wife. "I actually felt as if I were right there in the kitchen with the Matches. Yes, you shall certainly

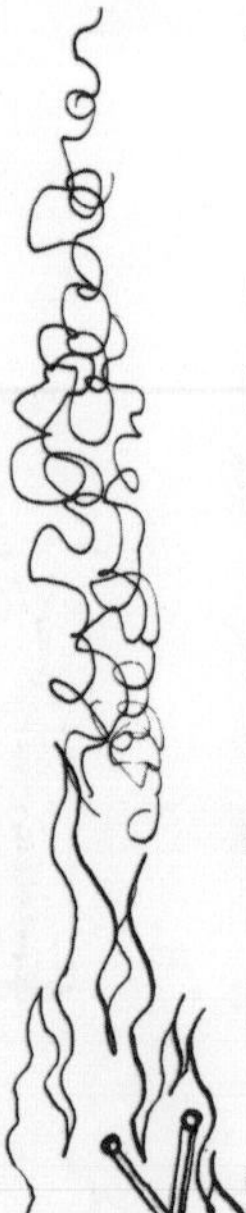

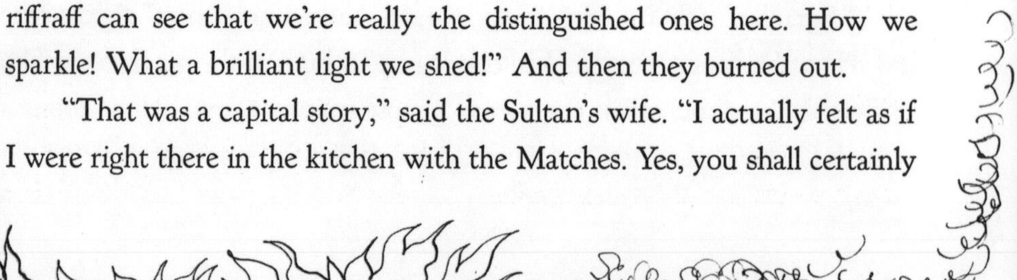

marry our daughter."

"You shall indeed," agreed the Sultan. "You'll marry her on Monday."

The evening before the wedding the whole town celebrated. The streets were lit up, goodies of every sort were flung to the people, street urchins whistled through their fingers and stood on tiptoe to cheer the parades at the top of their lungs. It was something to see.

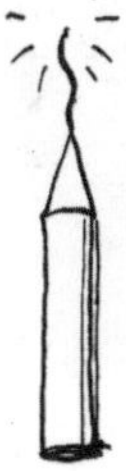

"I suppose I ought to add a thing or two to the merrymaking," thought the merchant's son. So he bought rockets and firecrackers and fireworks of every kind you can imagine, stuffed them into the trunk, and took off over the town.

Whizz! Bang! Crack! Whoosh! they went off, making the Turks hop about so briskly that their slippers flapped around their ears. Was there

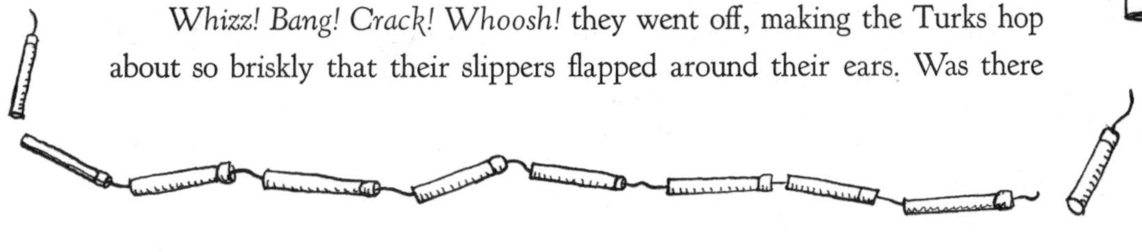

ever such a show? Such meteors? Such shooting stars? Now everyone was convinced that it was indeed the chief magician of the Turks who was to marry their Princess.

As soon as the merchant's son came down again, he left the trunk in the woods. "I'll just stroll around the town a bit," he said to himself, "to see what people are saying about my performance." It was only natural that he should want to know.

Heavens preserve us, the things people say! Every person he asked told him a different story but all agreed the spectacle had been superb.

"I saw the chief magician myself," said one. "His eyes were blazing stars and his beard was a flowing white stream."

"He wore a cloak of fire," said another, "and I could see with my own eyes the tiny heads of cherubs peeping out from the folds."

And so it went, one story more fantastic than the other, but all most pleasant to hear. And tomorrow was his wedding day.

He went back to the woods to get some rest in his trunk, but—mercy on us! Where was it? A spark from a firecracker left in the trunk had set it afire and now all that remained of it was a heap of ashes.

So he couldn't fly any more and he couldn't go to his bride. All day long she waited for him on the roof. No doubt she's waiting still. And he? He roams throughout the world telling stories, but not one of them is so gay as the one he told about the Matches.

The Ugly Duckling

It was summer and the country was delightful. In the fields the wheat lay golden and the oats were green and tall haystacks dotted the lush meadows. There the stork meandered about on his long red legs, chattering away in Egyptian, a language he had been taught by his mother.

Basking in the bright sunshine stood an old manor house with a deep moat around it. From the walls of the house to the water's edge grew burdock leaves so huge that little children could stand on tiptoe under the largest of them. It was just as dense here and as wild as in the thickest woods, and it was exactly here that a duck was sitting on her nest, hatching ducklings. Such a tiresome business, and what a long time it took.

At last, however, one after the other, the shells began to crack and, "Peep, peep," cried all the little ones as they stuck out their heads. Then "Quack, quack," they all said, tumbling as fast as they could out of the egg-

shells and gazing all about them under the big green leaves. Their mother let them look as long as they wished—she knew how good green is for the eyes.

"What a big wide world it is," said the ducklings, for now they had more room than they had before in the eggs.

"Do you think this is the whole world?" their mother asked. "Well, let me tell you something. The world is so big that it goes across the other side of the garden almost to the farmer's fields, but even I haven't ventured that far. Well," she went on and arose, "I hope you're all here. No—you're not. The largest egg is still not hatched. Dear me, *what* a boring business this is. I wonder how much longer I must stay with it?" And she sat down again.

"Hello there, how are things coming along?" asked an old duck, stopping by for a little visit.

"Oh, it's taking forever with this one egg which simply refuses to crack open," said the mother duck. "But come see the others. Aren't they pretty, the darlings!"

"Let me take a look at that stubborn egg," said the visitor. "It wouldn't surprise me if it's a turkey. I myself was fooled like this once. Here, do let me see that egg. Hmmm. No doubt about it—it's a turkey egg, all right. My advice is to let it alone and start teaching the others to swim."

"Oh well," said the duck, "another day or so won't matter."

"Do just as you like," said the old duck and off she waddled.

But the large egg did crack open at last and with a "Peep, peep," the youngster came out. He was big and ugly. The duck looked at him. "It's unusually large for a duckling," she mused. "None of the others looks like this. Can it be a turkey chick after all? Well, we'll soon see. He'll go into the water even if I have to shove him in myself."

The next day the weather was simply wonderful and the sun sparkled on all the green leaves. Mother Duck brought her entire family down to the water. Splash! In she went, and "Quack, quack," she called. All the duck-

lings, one after the other, followed her, even the big, ugly one. The water closed over their heads but they came up at once and began to swim smartly, their legs working naturally—no one had to tell them what to do. The big, ugly duckling swam along with the rest.

And so they arrived at the barnyard where there was a great to-do. Two families were fighting over an eel's head but the cat got it after all. "Oh well," said the mother duck, "that's how things go in this world."

"Now then," she went on, "pay strict attention. You're to look sharp and bow prettily to that old duck over there—she's the most important person here and everyone, man and beast, must respect her. All right, here we go, mind you don't turn your toes in. A well-bred duckling turns his toes out when he walks, like this. Now bow politely and say quack."

The ducklings did just as they were told but the other ducks in the yard looked them over and remarked loud enough for them to hear: "Must we put up with such riffraff? As if it isn't already overcrowded in here. And—there—especially that big, ugly one. We certainly don't have to accept him!" And one duck flew over and bit the ugly duckling.

"No, he isn't a turkey chick," said the mother duck, watching him. "See how nicely he uses his legs and how beautifully he holds himself. Yes, he's truly one of my own and not really too bad-looking when seen in the right light. . . . Quack, quack, now follow me, children, and I'll present you to the barnyard. But stay close to me so you won't get stepped on and keep an eye out for the cat."

"Oh, leave him alone," said the mother duck. "He isn't bothering any of you."

"That's so," said the duck who bit him, "but he's so ugly he deserves to be punished."

"You have very pretty children, Mother Duck," said the grand old one, "except that big, ugly one. It's too bad."

"Oh, he's all right, madam," said the mother duck. "Perhaps a bit odd-looking, but he is very good-natured and a wonderful swimmer. I'm sure he'll outgrow his awkwardness which came from lying too long in the egg. Besides, he's a boy, so he doesn't have to be pretty—just strong and good."

"Well, the other children are pretty enough," said the old one, "so make yourselves at home and if you find an eel's head, bring it to me."

So they made themselves at home; all, that is, except the ugly duckling. Poor thing, there was no place for him. Wherever he went he met with kicks and shoves and everyone made fun of him because he was so big and ugly. And so it went the first day, but matters did not improve after that. Indeed, things went from bad to worse.

The ducks bit him, the hens pecked him, and the hired girl, when she came out with their food, kicked him out of the way. The poor duckling stood it as long as he could and then decided to run away. As he skimmed over the hedge all the little birds in the bushes rose up in alarm. "It's because I'm so ugly," thought the duckling sadly, and he closed his eyes, but flew on until he reached a great, open marsh where wild ducks lived, and here he spent the night, completely exhausted and heavy of heart.

When the wild ducks saw the new arrival next morning, they didn't know what sort of creature he was. "You're uncommonly ugly," they told him, "but it's none of our business so long as you don't plan to marry into our family."

The poor duckling couldn't even begin to think of marrying. All he wanted was to be allowed to stay among the reeds and take a sip of water now and then. He remained there for two days when along came a pair of wild geese, or rather ganders. They weren't long out of the egg and that's why they were so fresh.

"See here, my boy," one of them said, "such ugliness as yours is positively attractive and we've taken a liking to you. Why don't you join us and become a vagabond too?"

Bang! Bang! came sharply through the air. Both vagabond ganders landed dead in the reeds. Bang! Bang! came again and a flock of wild geese rose up from the marsh. A great hunt was on. The hunters were hiding everywhere in the marsh; some even lurked in the branches of the trees that spread over the water. The hunting dogs came barking and charging, trampling down the reeds and rushes on all sides. The duckling trembled. He tried to hide his head under his wing but just then a huge setter appeared with lolling tongue and gleaming eyes. He sniffed at the duckling, opened wide his dreadful jaws to show his wicked teeth and then *splash! crash!* he was off without so much as a backward glance.

"Oh, Heaven be praised," sighed the duckling. "I'm so ugly that even the dogs won't touch me." He stayed in the marsh until late in the day when the shooting ceased and all grew quiet again. Even then he didn't dare leave but waited a few hours more. Then he made his way cautiously out of the marsh. He began to run over fields and through meadows, but such a stiff gale had blown up that he found the going very hard. However, by nightfall he at last reached a forlorn, shabby hut. He noticed that the door of the miserable hut hung crookedly on one hinge, leaving a crack just wide enough for him to squeeze through into the room. And that's just what he did.

An old woman lived in the hut with her cat and her hen. The old woman called the cat Sonny. He could arch his back and purr and if his fur was stroked the wrong way, he gave off sparks. The hen was called Shorty because she had such short little legs, but she laid good eggs and the old woman loved her as if she were her own child.

The next morning the stranger was noticed at once and the cat started to purr and the hen to cluck.

"What ails you both?" asked the old woman. She peered all around the room, but she couldn't see very well, so when she finally spotted the duckling she thought he was a fine fat duck that the storm had blown in.

"What luck!" she said. "Now I'll have a rare treat—duck's eggs."

So the duckling was allowed to stay on trial for three weeks but not one egg did he lay in all that time.

Now in this house the cat was master and the hen mistress, and they were forever saying, "We and the world," because they believed they were half the world and the better half at that. It seemed to the duckling that this was a matter of opinion and that other people might think differently but the hen would have none of this.

"Can you lay eggs?" she asked.

"No," answered the duckling.

"Then hold your tongue!"

"Can you arch your back and purr and give off sparks?" asked the cat.

"No," answered the duckling.

"Then of what use are your opinions? You'd best keep them to yourself when sensible people are talking."

The poor duckling sat down in a corner feeling very low. Then he began to think of the warm sunshine and the fresh air outdoors and such a yearning to swim came over him that he couldn't help but tell the hen.

"Are you out of your mind?" she cried. "These silly notions come from having nothing to do. You'd get over them all right if you'd only lay some eggs or learn to purr."

"I'd rather go out into the wide world," said the duckling.

"Oh well, it's no use—suit yourself," replied the hen.

So the duckling left. He swam beautifully on the water and dived expertly beneath it, but no living creature paid the slightest attention. He was ignored completely because he was so ugly.

Autumn came. The leaves turned yellow and brown and the sharp wind set them dancing in the cold air. The sky was bleak and the low clouds were filled with the threat of snow and hail. It was enough to make one shiver and the poor little duckling had a hard time indeed.

One evening a whole flock of dazzling white birds came out of the bushes. They were swans. They had long graceful necks and as they spread

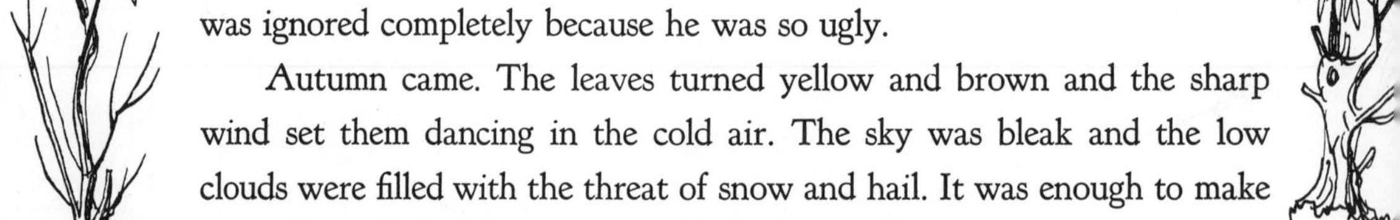

their tremendous beautiful wings they uttered a strange cry. They were leaving this cold region for warmer lands and open seas. They flew high,

high up and as he watched them a strange longing filled the duckling's heart. He swam frantically around and around, turning and craning his neck to follow them and crying out in such a peculiar voice that the sound frightened even himself. The duckling did not know who the beautiful birds were, nor where they were going, but he loved them more than he had ever loved anything. He didn't envy them their beauty, for how could he ever dream of such loveliness for himself? Poor lonely ugly thing, he would have been content just to be allowed to go with them.

Winter followed quickly. It was bitter cold. The duckling had to swim constantly and work his legs without resting to keep the water from freezing over entirely. But every day the open space in which he swam grew smaller and smaller and in spite of all his efforts, the ice closed in and at last, utterly worn out, the duckling sank down and was held fast in the ice.

Early in the morning a farmer passed by and saw him. He chipped away the ice with his wooden shoe, rescued the duckling, and took him home to his wife. There the duckling revived and the children tried to play with him. But he thought they meant to tease him so he flew away from them and landed in the milk pail, sending the milk sloshing all over the floor. The farmer's wife screamed and threw up her hands which so further frightened the duckling that he flew down into a tub of butter and from there into a barrel of flour and out again.

Heavens! What a sight he was now! The woman screamed again and went after him and the children fell all over each other as they chased him, shouting and yelling. Luckily the door was open and the duckling escaped into the reeds of the marsh.

I can't begin to tell you what a dreadful winter it was and how much the duckling suffered—it would be too sad. But when the sun grew warm again and the birds began to sing and lovely Spring returned, he was still there, in the marsh among the reeds. He tried his wings and found that he could flap them. They beat the air powerfully and the duckling realized they were very strong. They took him out of the marsh and before he knew it he was in a big garden where apple trees bloomed and the air was sweet with lilacs that hung in fragrant clusters from long green branches arching over a little lake. Out of the woods came three splendid swans. They ruffled their feathers and skimmed gracefully over the water. The duckling recognized them and a strange sadness filled his heart.

"I'll fly to those lordly birds," he thought, "even though no doubt they'll tear me to pieces because I who am so ugly dare approach them. But what difference would it make? I'd rather be killed by them than suffer the insults of the hens and the ducks, the kicks of the hired girl, and the cold and hunger of the cruel winter."

So he flew into the water and swam toward the lovely swans who, when they saw him, rushed to him with ruffled outstretched wings.

"Kill me," cried the poor duckling and bowed his head down on the water, awaiting their blows. But, what was this? Mirrored in the clear water was an image. Could it be his own? No gray dirty ugly duckling looked back at him from the water; instead, reflected there was a lovely white graceful swan.

You see, it doesn't matter if one is born in a duckyard, if only one has been hatched from a swan's egg.

Now the great swans stayed close to the duckling, stroking him with their beaks. Soon some little children came into the garden with bits of bread and corn. They threw these into the water and the youngest cried, "Look, there's a new one here." They clapped their hands and capered about merrily and dashed off to bring their father and mother.

Everyone threw bread and cake into the water and all agreed that the new swan was the most beautiful of all.

The duckling was overcome with shyness and hid his head under his wing. He was very happy but not a bit proud. He recalled how he had been hated and scorned and now here was everyone calling him the most beautiful of all beautiful birds. He rustled his gleaming feathers, held high his graceful neck, and cried happily from the depths of his grateful heart, "Oh, I never dreamed there could be so much happiness when I was the ugly duckling."

The Swineherd

There was once a Prince who wasn't rich, but he had a kingdom. True, the kingdom was small. Still, his having it meant he could afford to marry and this he wanted very much to do.

Nevertheless, it was rather brazen of him to say to the Emperor's daughter, "Will you marry me?" But so he did, for he was known far and wide and there were a hundred princesses who would have accepted gladly and said, "Thank you, sir." But did *she?* Well, let's see what happened.

A rose tree grew near the grave of the Prince's father. It was a lovely tree but it bloomed only once every five years and then produced but one flower. Ah, what a rose was that! It smelled so sweet it made one forget every pain and heartache. What was more, the Prince had a nightingale who sang as if every wonderful melody in the world lived in her tiny throat.

The Prince decided to give the rose and the nightingale to the Princess, so they were packed up in silver boxes and sent to her. The Emperor had the boxes brought into the large hall where the Princess and her ladies-in-waiting were playing "Visiting"—they didn't have much else to do. When the Princess saw the presents, she clapped her hands and cried joyfully, "Oh, I do wish a darling little kitten is in this box." Out came the lovely rose.

"Isn't it enchanting?" cried the ladies-in-waiting.

"It's more than enchanting," said the Emperor. "It's most exquisitely made."

The Princess put out a finger, touched the rose, and almost burst into

tears. "Oh, pshaw, Papa," she cried. "It's not made at all. It's real."

And "Pshaw," cried all the ladies-in-waiting, "it's real."

"Well, let's see what's in the other box," said the Emperor, "before we lose our tempers."

Out came the nightingale. It sang so beautifully that at first no one could think of a thing to say against it.

"*Superbe!*" "*Charmant!*" cried the ladies-in-waiting. They all jabbered in French, one worse than the other.

"How that bird reminds me of the music box that belonged to our sainted Empress," sighed an old officer of the Court. "Ah yes, it has the same tone and gives the same perfect performance."

"Yes, it does," said the Emperor, and he wept like a child.

"I still hope it's not a real bird," said the Princess, but those who brought it assured her the bird was real.

"Well then," said the Princess, "if it's real, let it fly away." And she wouldn't see the Prince under any circumstances.

However, he wasn't the sort of lad who took No for an answer. He smudged his face, pulled his cap down over his ears, and knocked at the palace door. "Good morning, Emperor," he said. "Perhaps there's a job of some kind here for me?"

"Everyone's hunting a job these days," said the Emperor. "Let's see —yes, we could use more help to look after the pigs."

So the Prince was appointed Imperial Swineherd and a miserable, dirty little hole-in-the-wall near the pigsties was given him for a room. There he spent the whole day hard at work, and when evening came he had fashioned a most delightful saucepan. It had little bells all around it; when the pan was boiling the bells tinkled charmingly and played the old song:

Alas, alas, dear Augustin,
All is gone, gone, gone.

But what was even more remarkable about the saucepan was this: whenever anyone held his finger in the smoke that came from it he could at once smell all the dinners cooking everywhere in the town.

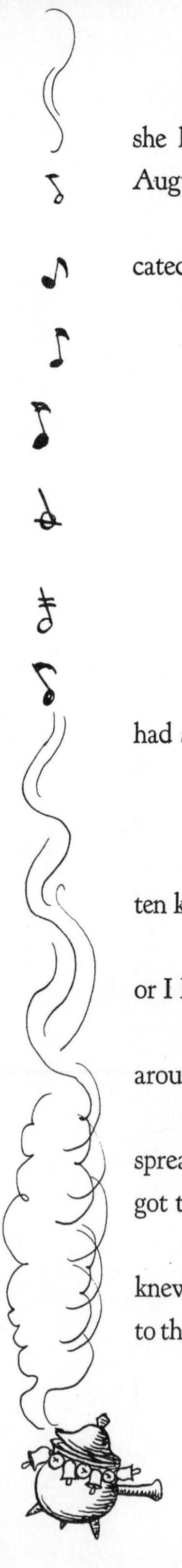

The Princess came strolling by with her ladies-in-waiting and when she heard the tune she stopped to listen. She was quite pleased. "Dear Augustin" was the only piece she knew—she played it herself with one finger.

"Why, it's my piece," she said. "That swineherd is certainly well educated. Here, one of you, go and ask him what he wants for the instrument."

One of the ladies went in, but first she had to put on her rubbers.

"What do you want for the saucepan?" she asked.

"I want ten kisses from the Princess," said the swineherd.

"Heaven help us!" exclaimed the lady-in-waiting.

"I simply cannot take less," said the swineherd.

"Well, what does he want?" asked the Princess.

"Really, I don't dare tell you," answered the lady. "It's too dreadful!"

"Then whisper it."

So the lady-in-waiting whispered the shocking price.

"He's an insolent wretch," said the Princess and walked on. But hardly had she taken a few steps when the bells began to tinkle *so* engagingly:

Alas, alas, dear Augustin,
All is gone, gone, gone.

"Wait a minute," said the Princess. "Go back and ask him if he'll take ten kisses from my ladies-in-waiting."

"No, thank you," said the swineherd. "Ten kisses from the Princess, or I keep my saucepan."

"What a nuisance he is," said the Princess. "However . . . form a ring around me and let no one see."

So all the ladies-in-waiting stood in front of the Princess in a ring and spread out their skirts, and the swineherd got his ten kisses and the Princess got the saucepan.

And now, what fun! The pan was kept boiling constantly and they knew what was cooking on every stove in town from the prime minister's to the shoemaker's. The ladies-in-waiting danced about, clapping their hands.

"We know who has soup and who has pancakes for dinner; who has

chops and who has an omelet. How exciting!"

"Very exciting," said the Princess, "but don't give me away for I am the Emperor's daughter."

"Heaven help us," they all cried.

The swineherd, that is, the Prince—though no one knew he wasn't really a swineherd—didn't let a day go by without making something.

At last he put together a rattle which, when it was swung around, played all the waltzes, reels, and jig tunes ever heard since the world began.

"This is *superbe,*" said the Princess when she happened along. "They're really the most excellent compositions. Go in and ask him what he wants for this instrument. But mind—there's to be no more kissing."

"He wants a hundred kisses from the Princess," gasped the lady-in-waiting.

"He's stark raving mad," cried the Princess, and walked on in a huff. But she didn't get very far before she stopped. "After all," she said, "one should encourage artistic talent. I am the Emperor's daughter, so I ought to set a good example. Go back; tell him he can have ten kisses from me as before and he must take the rest from my ladies."

The lady-in-waiting had no choice but to go back again.

"A hundred kisses from the Princess," said the swineherd, "or each keeps his own."

"Oh, all right," said the Princess. "But form a ring around me again."

All the ladies-in-waiting took their places and the kissing began.

"What's going on near the pigsties?" wondered the Emperor who happened to step out on the balcony. "I've never seen such a crowd. I'll bet the girls are up to something as usual. I'd better go see."

So he pulled up his badly-run-down-at-the-heels slippers and—ho! there—just see him hurry along! When he got to the yard he trod very softly. The ladies-in-waiting were so busy counting the kisses to make sure all went fair and square that no one heard him approach. The Emperor rose on tiptoes.

"Hey! What's this?" And when he saw what was going on, he boxed the Princess's ears soundly with his slipper just as the swineherd was taking the eighty-sixth kiss.

"Out!" roared the Emperor. "Out you go!" He was so furious that he banished both the Princess and the swineherd from the palace.

So there they were, outside the palace gates. The Princess sobbed, the swineherd scolded, and the rain came pouring down.

"Oh, woe is me," wailed the Princess. "Why didn't I accept the handsome Prince? Oh, poor, poor me!"

The swineherd went behind a tree, washed the black smudges off his face, threw aside his soiled clothes, and stepped forth in his princely robes. He looked so handsome and so royal that the Princess couldn't help curtsying to him.

"I have nothing but scorn for you," he said. "You wouldn't have an honorable Prince; you placed no value on the rose and the nightingale, yet you were willing to kiss the swineherd for a foolish toy. You've got just what you deserve."

And he returned to his own little kingdom and shut the door in her face. Now she has good reason to sigh,

Alas, alas, dear Augustin,
All is gone, gone, gone.

In Johnny Crow's Garden.

"GOOD-BYE!"

And they all sat down
to their dinner in a row

But Johnny Crow
He let them go

In Johnny Crow's Garden.

Put them all in the Stocks

And the Fox

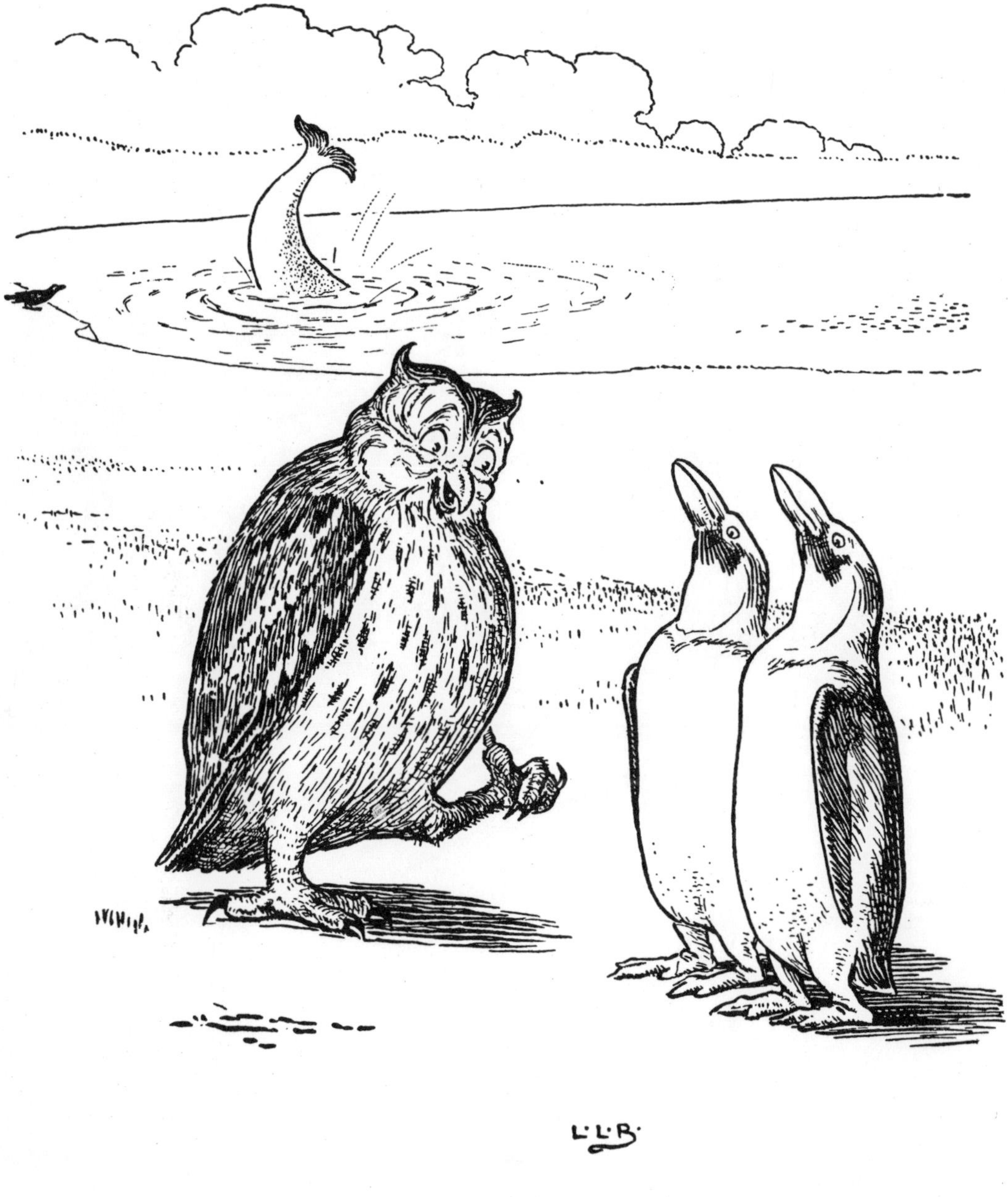

And the Owl
Was a funny old Fowl

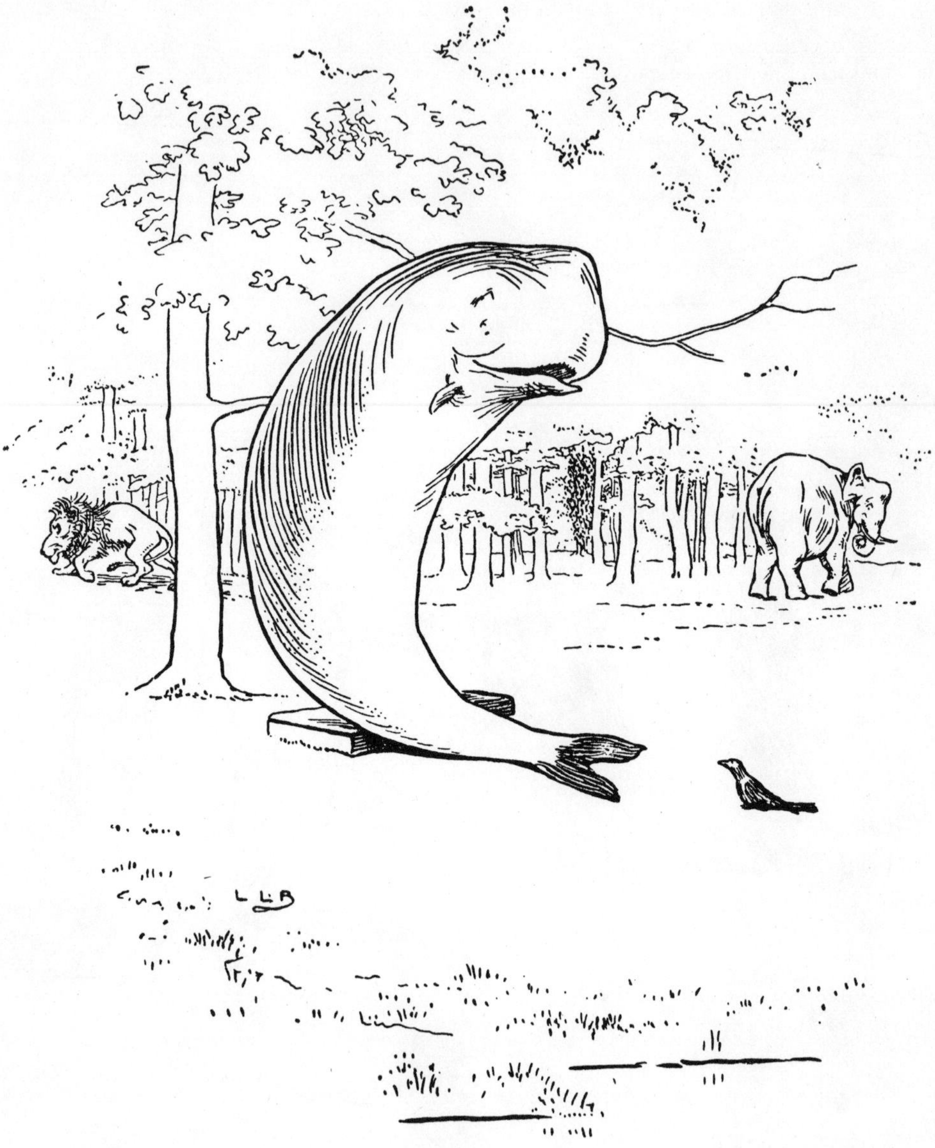

In Johnny Crow's Garden.

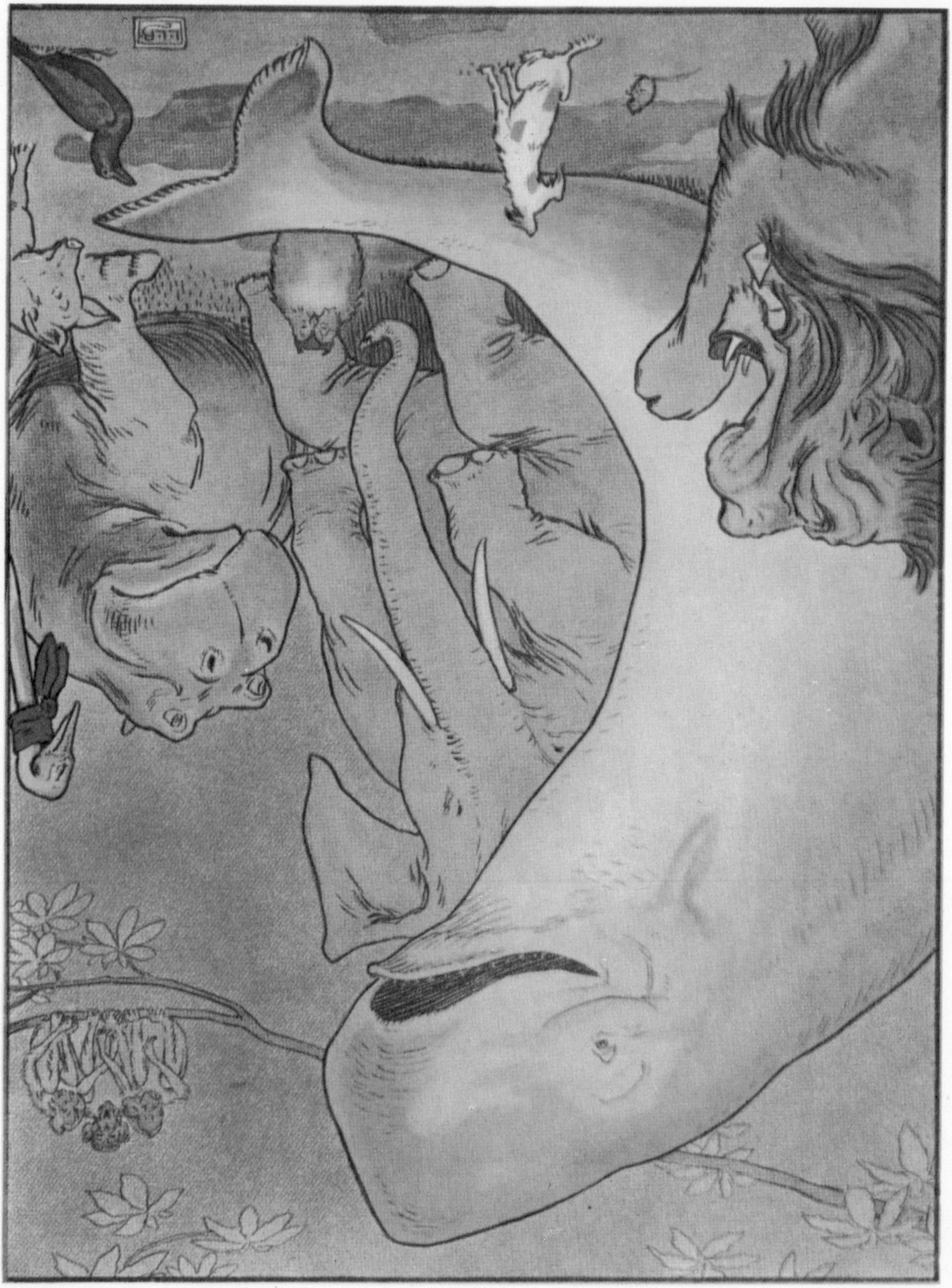

Told a very long Tale

And the Whale

In Johnny Crow's Garden.

Sat down beside the Mat

Where the Cat

Built himself a little House

And the Mouse

In Johnny Crow's Garden.

ADLY
D TO
THE
RASS
J. Crow.

the Goose *was* a Goose

YOU ARE KINDLY
REQUESTED TO
KEEP OFF THE
GRASS
J. Crow
L.L.B.

And the Goose—
Well,

In Johnny Crow's Garden.

While the Elephant
Said something quite irrelevant

Till the Hippopotami
Said: "Ask no further 'What am I?'"

Then the Stork
Gave a Philosophic Talk

In Johnny Crow's Garden.

And the Pig
Danced a Jig

In Johnny Crow's Garden.

"It's nothing but his Throat!"

But the Goat
Said :

And the Beaver
Was afraid he had a Fever

In Johnny Crow's Garden.

Was caught in the Rain

Then the Crane

In Johnny Crow's Garden.

Took his Measure with a Tape

So the Ape

In Johnny Crow's Garden.

But the Bear
Had nothing to wear

And the Rat
Wore a Feather in his Hat

In Johnny Crow's Garden.

Had a green and yellow Tie on

And the Lion

Till he made a little Garden.

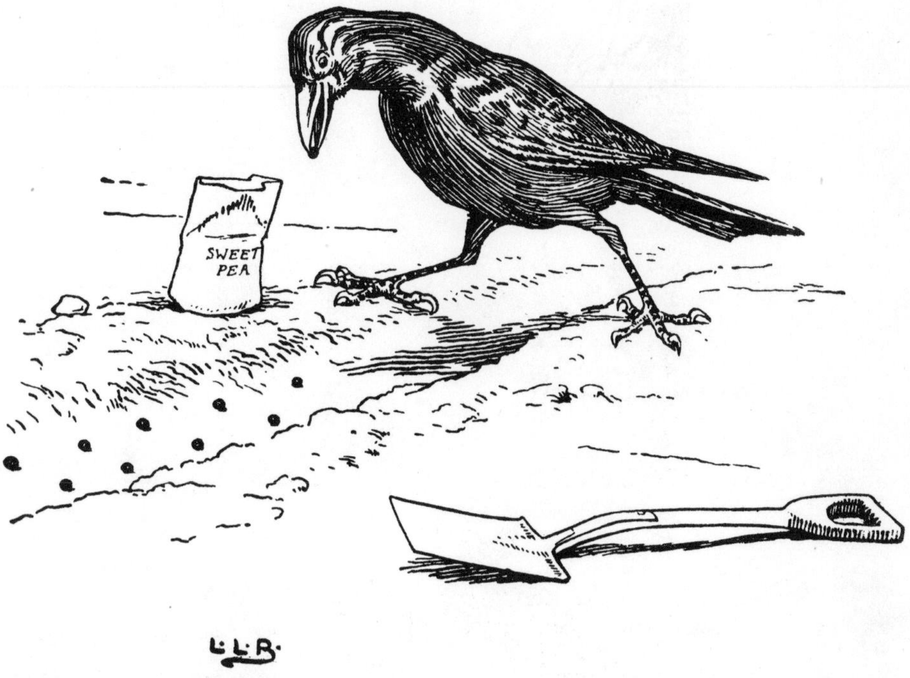

Johnny Crow
Would dig and sow

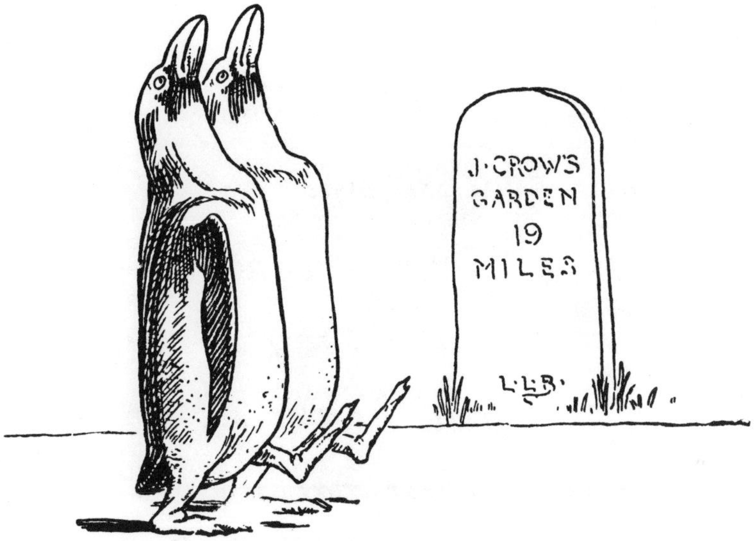
J·CROW'S
GARDEN
19
MILES
L·L·B·

To the Memory of
my Father, who first told
me of Johnny Crow's
Garden: and to my Boys,
for whom I have set on
record these facts con-
cerning it..

From the original edition published by
Frederick Warne & Co.

JOHNNY CROW'S GARDEN

A PICTURE BOOK

DRAWN BY

L·LESLIE BROOKE

GROLIER ENTERPRISES INC. • NEW YORK

This Way to
JOHNNY CROW'S
GARDEN